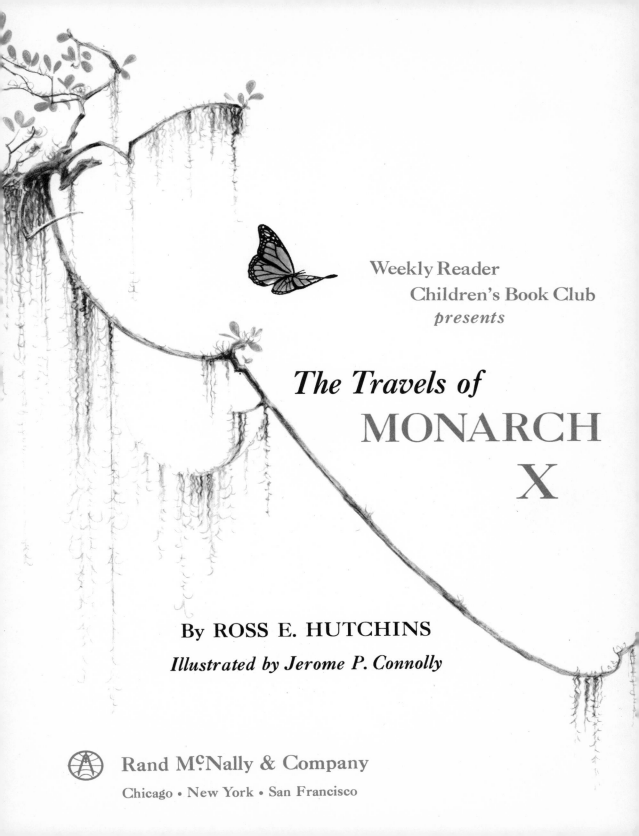

Weekly Reader
Children's Book Club
presents

The Travels of
MONARCH X

By **ROSS E. HUTCHINS**

Illustrated by Jerome P. Connolly

Rand McNally & Company

Chicago • New York • San Francisco

To DR. FRED URQUHART, *University of Toronto, Canada.*

THE MILKWEED PLANT grew in a meadow in
Canada just north of Lake Ontario.

In mid-August, a Monarch butterfly laid an egg on
one of its leaves. The egg was no larger than the head of
a pin. It sparkled in the sun like a tiny jewel.

After a few days the egg hatched and a tiny caterpillar crawled out of the thin shell.

The caterpillar immediately ate the eggshell; then it began to eat the milkweed leaf.

As the days went by, the caterpillar ate many other milkweed leaves, and it grew very quickly.

When two weeks had passed, the Monarch cater-pillar was two inches long.

It was now 2,700 times as big as when it hatched from the egg.

Its body was circled with black and yellow bands, and it had two horns at each end.

One day the caterpillar crawled away from the milkweed on which it had been feeding, looking for a place to change into the *chrysalis* stage.

It looked everywhere.

At last it found a good place in a field on the underside of a rail fence.

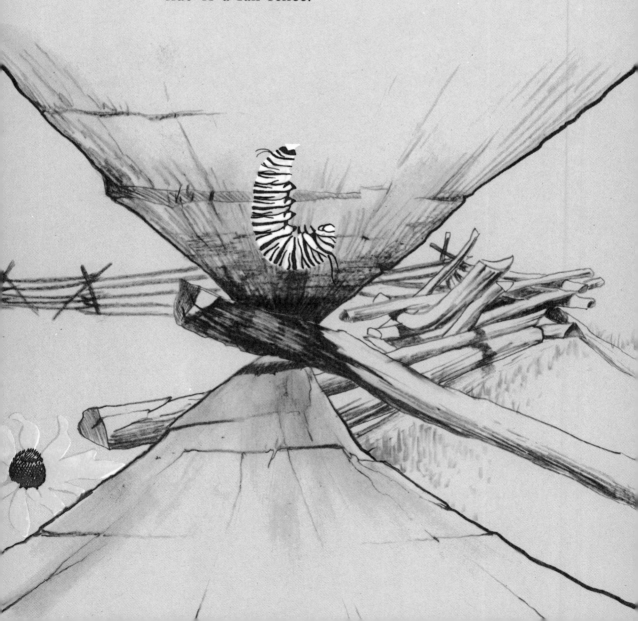

Here it spun a small patch of silk into which it hooked its hind legs.

Then it hung head-downward.

Its old skin split open and was slowly pushed off.

Inside the old skin was the chrysalis case.
This case enclosed the future butterfly.

The chrysalis was very beautiful.

It was pale green, marked with golden spots that glistened in the summer sun.

One morning, two weeks later, the chrysalis split open.

Slowly the winged Monarch butterfly crawled out. At first the wings were damp and crumpled up.

But little by little the new Monarch's wings expanded and dried out.

They were rust-red, marked with black, and covered with tiny scales. The scales were like little shingles.

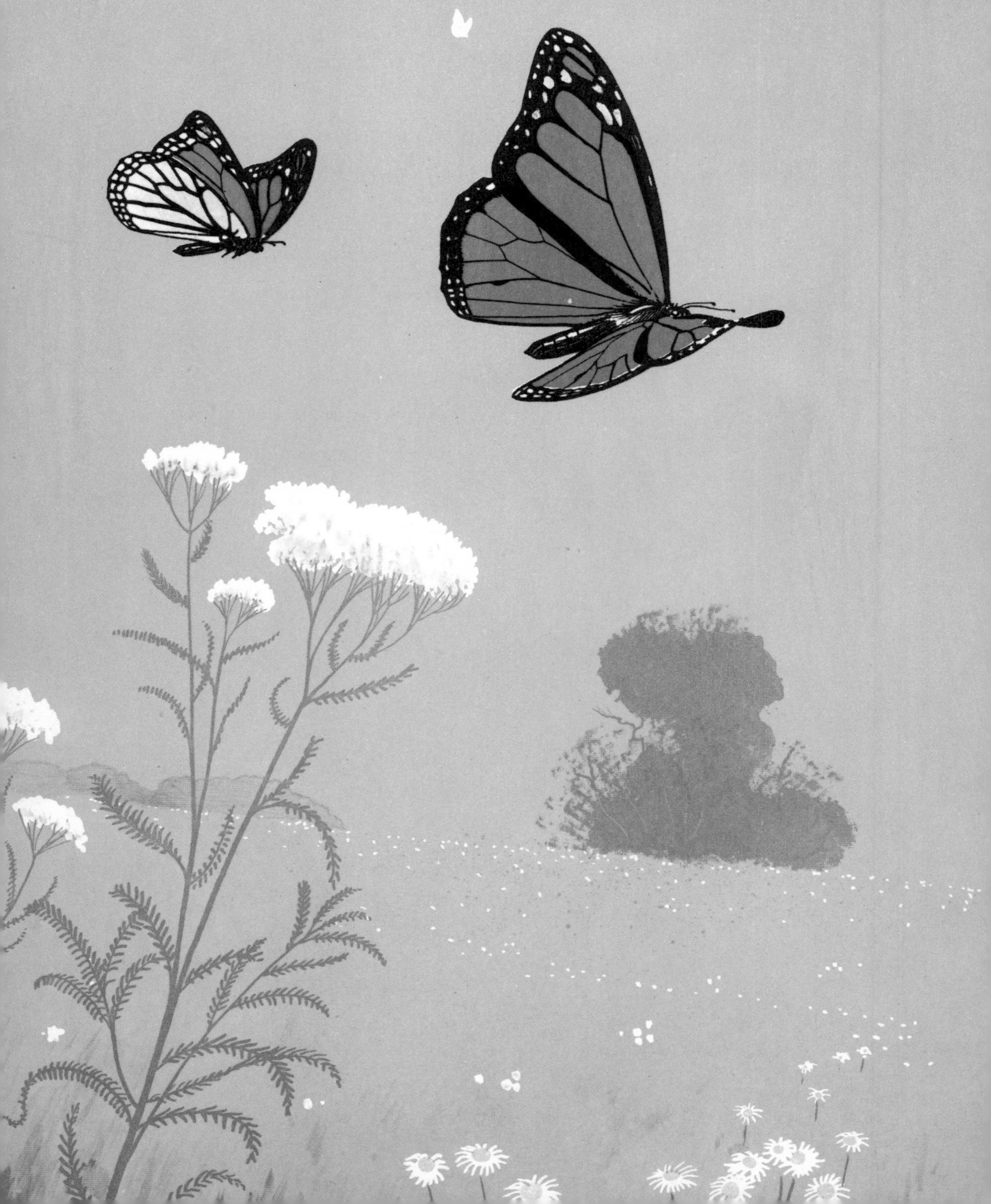

When the Monarch's wings were completely dry, it sailed away across the field.

There were many other Monarch butterflies in the field. In daytime they flitted about with never a care.

The field was near Highland Creek, near Toronto, Canada.

When the fall nights became cooler, the Monarchs began to roost together at night. They looked like dead, brown leaves on the tree limbs.

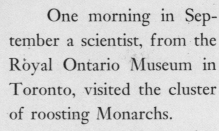

ON 1050
Send to
Museum
Toronto,
Canada

One morning in September a scientist, from the Royal Ontario Museum in Toronto, visited the cluster of roosting Monarchs.

To each Monarch's right, front wing he glued a tiny tag. The tag on Monarch X said: "Send to Museum, Toronto, Canada." It also bore a number.

The scientist recorded the tag number in his notebook, as he glued each tag to a Monarch's wing.

He hoped that anyone who found one of these tagged Monarchs would send it back to the Royal Ontario Museum, telling where he found it.

If any of the tagged Monarch butterflies were sent back, the scientist would know where they had gone.

By late September many birds had already left for warmer climates.

With the coming of shorter days the Monarchs, also, were stimulated to begin their southbound flights.

As soon as the sun was high enough to warm the butterflies, they spread their wings and fluttered away. Monarch X flew along with the others.

The large flock of migrating Monarchs soon came to the shore of Lake Ontario. Here they flew about, sipping nectar from various flowers.

A few of the Monarchs flew along the shore.

Monarch X and the rest flew southward over the lake. Below them the water sparkled in the autumn sunshine.

Soon they were out of sight of land.

Near the center of the lake, heavy rain began to fall.

This made it hard for the Monarchs to fly. Some of them fell into the water and were drowned.

Monarch X also fell into the water. But it managed to flutter up again and fly on across the lake with the others that were left.

Soon the sun came out again and dried its wings.

Within a few hours the Monarchs reached the southern shore of Lake Ontario.

Beyond the southern shore of the lake, the Monarchs came to a wooded area and beyond this was an open field, where many flowers grew.

Here they settled down to drink flower nectar; then they flew southward again.

Day after day they continued their travels, often flying a hundred feet above the ground.

Every night they settled down to roost together in trees.

Each morning, after the sun came up and warmed them, they flew on.

One day they stopped in a field to sip nectar in a flower garden.

A small boy with a butterfly net saw Monarch X on a zinnia. He swung his net over the flower and the butterfly fluttered about inside.

The boy intended to add the pretty Monarch to his butterfly collection.

He was very pleased to have the beautiful creature. He reached into the net, picked the Monarch up, and took it out of the net.

Monarch X was very excited. Suddenly it flapped its wings, slipped out of the boy's fingers, and flew away.

The small boy was sad. He stood watching the butterfly as it flew rapidly away across the garden.

Soon Monarch X found the rest of the flock and together they sailed away over the fields.

They came to a range of high mountains, but they did not stop. They flew up the mountainside in a southerly direction as if they had the kind of compasses airplanes have.

At the top of the mountain it was very cool.

High overhead there were many birds. They, too, were flying south for the winter.

The flock of Monarchs settled down in a pine grove for the night.

The next morning, after the sun warmed the mountaintop, the Monarchs sailed down the other side of the mountain.

Always they flew southward.

They crossed over deep canyons where streams tumbled over rocky beds. Then they came to level forests near cities, and towns, and highways.

They were now in the state of Virginia. They paused now and then to drink nectar from red butterflyweeds that bloomed in the fields.

Some of the Monarchs strayed away from the flock and disappeared.

A few others were eaten by catbirds and cuckoos. Most other kinds of birds do not like to eat Monarchs.

Monarch X and the others that were left flew on southward.

The flock was not traveling very fast. Usually, they flew along at about 11 miles per hour.

Sometimes, when they were chased by birds, the Monarchs speeded up to 25 miles per hour.

It was late in October when they reached the Carolinas.

The forests were now tinted by autumn's gold and red.

In the meadows goldenrod was blooming.

Sometimes the Monarchs settled down to drink nectar.

Like airplanes, they needed fuel to enable them to fly. A Monarch can fly for hundreds of miles on one "tankful" of flower nectar.

The Monarch flock continued on southward as if guided by some built-in compass.

They crossed the state of Georgia and came to the great Okefenokee Swamp. Here they flew through a great forest, whose cypress trees were draped with streamers of Spanish moss that swayed in the breeze.

Below them were dark waters, where alligators and turtles lay sleeping upon fallen logs.

One night the Monarchs roosted in a large live-oak tree that grew on an island. They nestled down among the strands of moss.

Late in the night, a mouselike shrew found the sleeping Monarchs and ate many of them. Only their wings were left.

When dawn came, there were many Monarch wings scattered like dead leaves upon the ground beneath the oak.

The sun rose over the brown waters of the swamp and, one by one, the rest of the Monarchs flew away.

Monarch X was unharmed; it had escaped the hungry shrew.

The Okefenokee Swamp was very large. It took many days for the flock of Monarchs to fly through it.

Each night, while the butterflies slept in trees, the autumn moon hung over the watery forest.

Sometimes the call of the great horned owl could be heard.

Deep in the swamp, beneath a spreading live oak, there was a dark pool where a very old bass lived.

One day in early November the Monarch flock glided across the pool.

Monarch X flew just above the water's surface.

The bass saw the butterfly and lunged out of the water with its jaws wide open.

But the Monarch saw the great fish and darted away just in time.

There was a loud splash as the bass fell back into the water.

After leaving the Okefenokee Swamp, the Monarchs turned westward.

They crossed the lazy, brown Suwannee River as it meandered southward toward the Gulf of Mexico.

The weather was warmer now and, at night, damp fog drifted out of the lowlands.

Some mornings the roosting Monarchs were wet with dew.

But each morning, after the sun had warmed and dried them, they flew on toward the west.

Soon they came to the wide Pascagoula Swamp, where there were many islands.

The islands were covered with fanlike palmettos that rustled in the breeze.

The Monarchs flew across the swamp and over the wide river.

There were other butterflies flying across the swamp too.

These were cloudless sulphur butterflies.

They were flying eastward while the Monarchs traveled westward. Different kinds of butterflies often migrate in different directions.

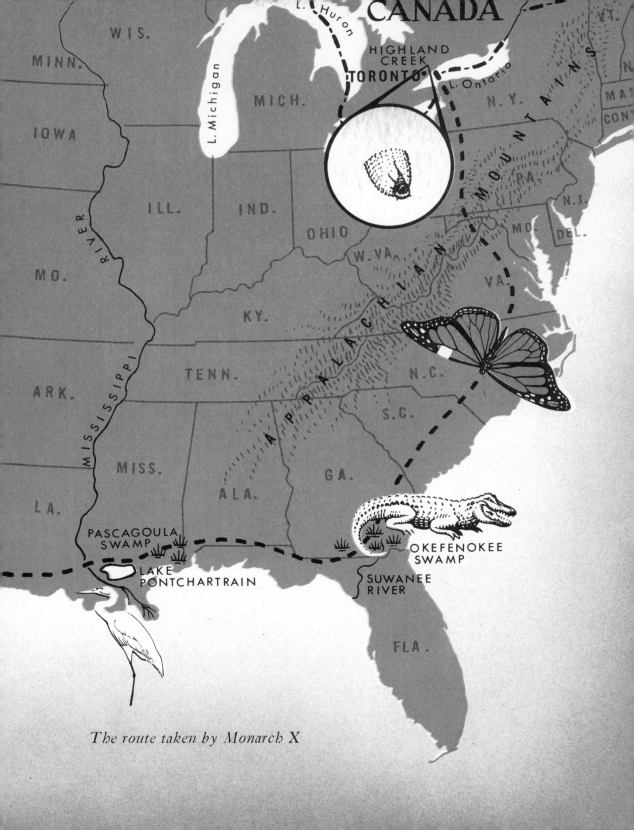

The route taken by Monarch X

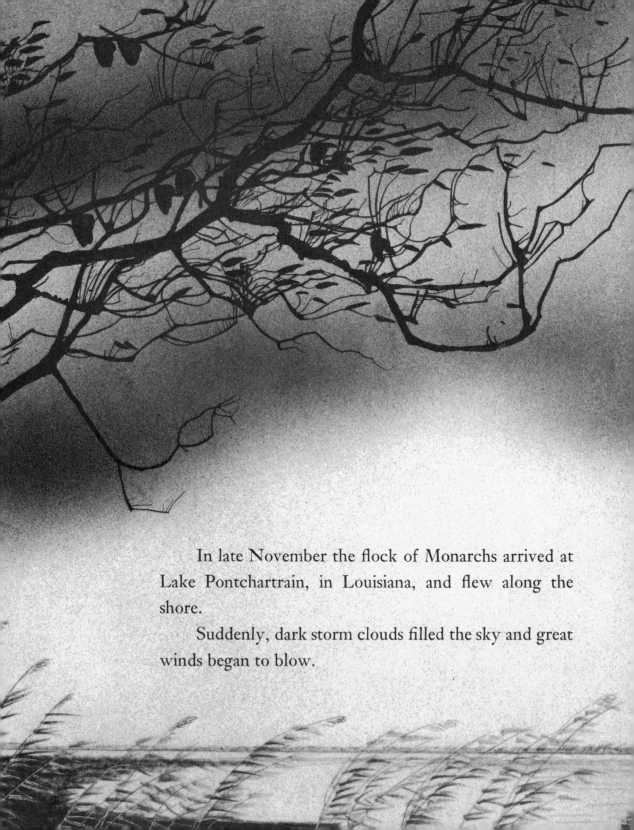

In late November the flock of Monarchs arrived at Lake Pontchartrain, in Louisiana, and flew along the shore.

Suddenly, dark storm clouds filled the sky and great winds began to blow.

A hurricane had struck the Gulf Coast and was slowly blowing inland.

The Monarchs settled in the bushes and clung to twigs and leaves. Their wings were wet and limp.

For several days the winds lashed the forest, and some of the Monarchs were killed.

But the sun came out at last and the winds and rain were gone.

What was left of the flock flew on, still westward.

They crossed over the great marsh-grass prairies of Louisiana.

Beneath them the tall grass swayed in the breeze.

White egrets waded about in the water looking for minnows.

In early December, the butterfly flock left the
Louisiana marshes and came to Texas.

The sun was even warmer now and autumn flowers
still bloomed in many places.

Sometimes the Monarchs settled down to drink
nectar.

In Texas, there were fewer trees, so at night the
flock formed roosting clusters in low mesquite bushes.

While flying along in the daytime, some of the
Monarchs were captured by hungry birds.

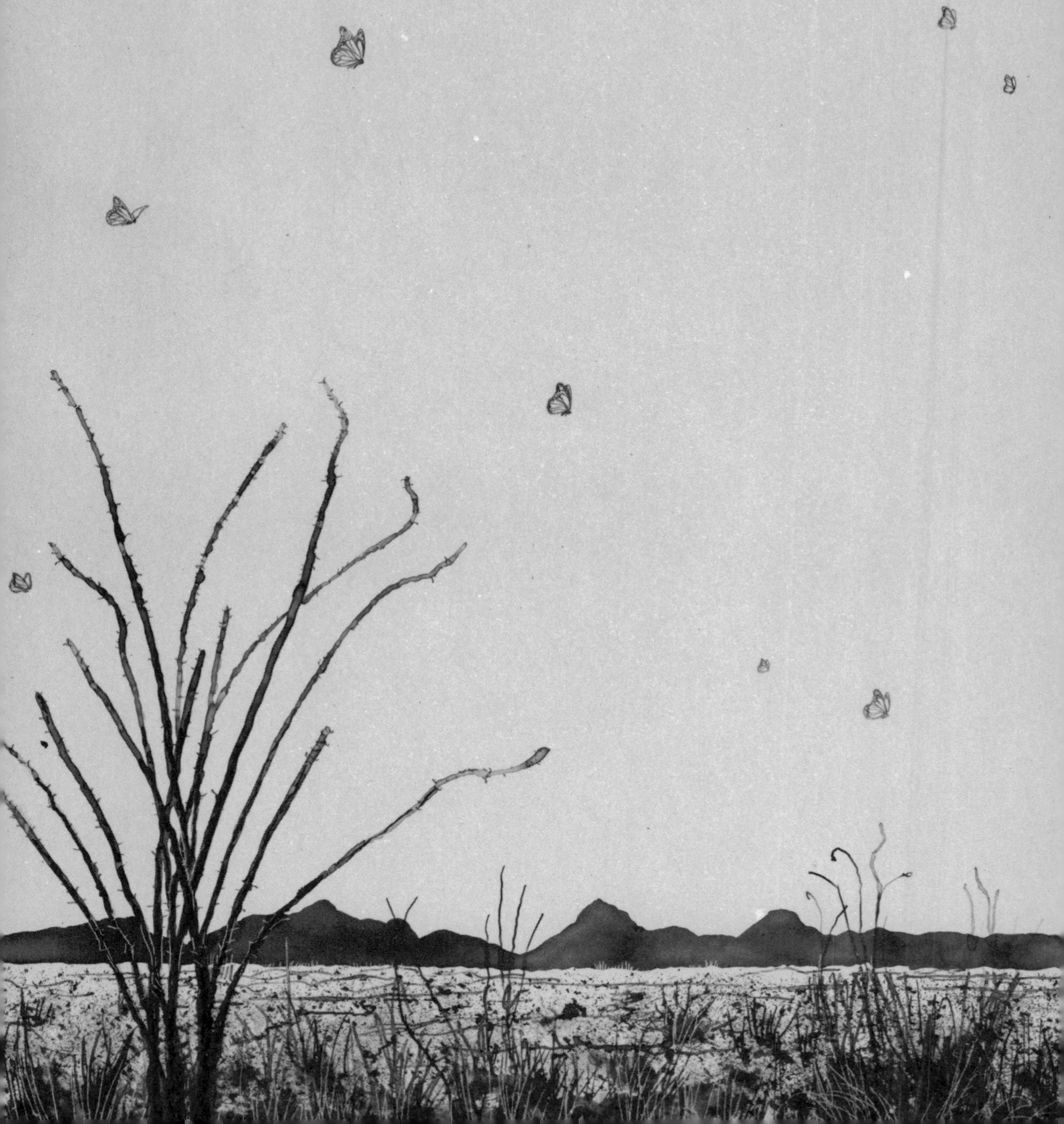

Gradually the Monarchs began to change their direction of flight.

Soon they were traveling southward again.

One day in December the flock crossed the Rio Grande at Eagle Pass, Texas and flew into Mexico.

The size of the flock was slowly decreasing.

In Mexico, the country was dry and desert-like. The ground was sandy and covered with low trees and cactus.

There were few flowers from which the butterflies could drink nectar.

Soon the Monarchs came to the barren Sierra Madre Mountains. Some of the ranges were more than 10,000 feet high.

But the Monarchs flew through a pass or gap in the mountains.

High overhead, buzzards circled in the sky. They were not interested in the Monarchs; they were looking for larger game.

Beyond the high mountains there were low mountains and then hills.

Sometimes the Monarchs passed tiny Mexican villages.

Always they flew toward the south.

In early January the flock of migrating Monarchs came to a river called the Sabinas.

They followed the river down to a large lake, where there were many people fishing along the shore.

Some of the people looked up and watched the long string of butterflies.

Then they went on fishing again.

One day the flock came to a railroad track that stretched away toward the south.

They followed it for several days.

Along the railroad track there was a village, where many flowers grew around a church.

Monarch X dropped down to sip nectar from the bright blooms.

The rest of the flock flew on toward the south.

Monarch X was left behind.

Monarch X soon drank its fill of nectar and flew away across the low hills.

On January 25, it flew down a dry *arroyo*, or canyon, where some Mexican children were playing. They were from the nearby village of Catorce in the state of San Luis Potosí.

One boy ran after the lone Monarch and captured it under his *sombrero*.

Curiously, the little Mexican boy looked at the pretty butterfly and saw the tag that had been placed on its right wing in far-off Canada.

The tag had English words on it, and he could read only Spanish.

Holding the struggling butterfly in his hand, he hurried home and copied down the numbers and the strange words.

Then he tossed the butterfly out of the window and it sailed rapidly away across the cactus-covered hills.

Later, he showed his teacher the paper with the numbers and words he had written. She wrote to the Museum at Toronto, Canada, telling them about the capture of the tagged Monarch.

The scientist at the museum was very pleased when he received the letter.

The capture of this tagged butterfly in far-off Mexico proved that it had flown for nearly 2,000 miles.

As far as is known, it had flown farther than any of the thousands of other Monarchs that had been tagged.

Its paper-thin wings had carried it southward across a vast continent. It had survived storms and escaped many enemies along the way.

That is the amazing story of Monarch X, a frail butterfly that established a world's record for long-distance travel.

We will never know how Monarch X ended its days.

AUTHOR'S NOTE

This is a true story of a Monarch butterfly. It was one of thousands of Monarchs tagged by Dr. Fred Urquhart of the University of Toronto, Canada in his interesting studies of butterfly migration. After being released, this Monarch flew southward across the United States and on to Estación Catorce (Station Fourteen) in the State of San Luis Potosí, Mexico, where it was captured again.

Unfortunately, the records relating to this Monarch butterfly have been destroyed, so we do not know what the number was on the tag attached to its wing, nor do we know whether it was a male or a female. And we do not know the name of the Mexican boy who captured it. So, in this story, we will call our butterfly Monarch X. Only the beginning and the end of the journey of Monarch X are definitely known; what happened along the way we can only guess. Scientific evidence gathered from the recapture of other Monarchs indicates, however, that Monarch X probably did not fly directly toward its final destination in Mexico, but followed a curving route that took it southward to the vicinity of Georgia and then westward along the Gulf of Mexico. When captured at Estación Catorce, Monarch X was in good condition in spite of its long and hazardous flight.

Through autumn gales, across rivers, and through forests where there were many enemies, it traveled. Day by day, from September 18, 1957 to January 25 of the following year, Monarch X winged its way along with many others. In imagination, we have followed its wanderings as it flew, like a migrating bird, across this vast continent to its final destination nearly two thousand miles away.

—R.E.H.

ATTENTION Would you like to work with Dr. Urquhart as a research associate in his interesting research on butterfly migration? If so, you should write to: Dr. Fred A. Urquhart, Associate Professor, Department of Zoology, University of Toronto, Canada. He can supply you with information and the special, numbered tags to be attached to Monarch butterfly wings. Perhaps, in this way, you can make an interesting contribution to the study of Monarch migration and the flight paths they follow. Perhaps, too, one of your tagged Monarchs might fly even farther than Monarch X did.

SCIENTIFIC NOTES

Monarch Butterfly: The scientific name of this attractive butterfly is *Danaus plexippus.* It is a common butterfly in nearly all of the United States and in Canada, Mexico, and other countries. The Monarch, and all other butterflies, have four stages in their life history. These are: egg, caterpillar (larva), chrysalis (pupa), and adult winged butterfly. The female butterfly lays her eggs only on milkweed plants and the tiny caterpillars, which hatch from the eggs, begin feeding upon the leaves. At the end of two weeks they are about two inches long. Each caterpillar then suspends itself from the underside of some object, such as a fence rail, and changes into the inactive chrysalis which lasts for another two weeks. The chrysalis is very pretty; it is bright green with golden spots. While in the chrysalis stage the body of the insect slowly changes in form from a creeping caterpillar into the winged butterfly. Just before the butterfly is ready to emerge from the chrysalis its wings can be seen through the cellophane-like skin. Soon the skin splits open and the butterfly crawls out. At first its wings are crumpled and wet, but they quickly dry out and harden and the pretty butterfly then flies away.

Monarch Migration: Like birds, these butterflies fly south in autumn and north in spring. Sometimes they travel in large flocks, which have often been seen in various parts of North America. The individuals that fly south in autumn are not the same ones that flew north the previous spring. Their descendants make the southward flight. For a number of years, scientists have been studying these migrating butterflies. They attach small paper tags to their wings and then release them, hoping that some of them will, later, be captured and returned to the scientists who tagged them. In this way they learn where and how far away the Monarchs traveled. From such studies it appears that Monarchs tagged in autumn in

Ontario, Canada, for example, fly southward toward Florida and, when near the Gulf Coast, turn westward and fly toward Texas and Mexico. Not all the Monarchs follow this path. Tagged Monarchs have been captured in many eastern states that are not in the usual flight path. West of the Rocky Mountains, Monarchs also migrate or fly south in autumn and northward in spring.

At the southern ends of their flight the butterflies often roost in trees and bushes in large numbers. Sometimes Monarchs use the same places year after year, though the individuals are different ones. For instance, Monarchs have been roosting in the same trees at Pacific Grove, California, for many years. Such roosting places have also been found in Florida, Texas, and other southern states. Why they form these roosting clusters is something of a mystery but, apparently, it occurs when weather becomes cooler. Sometimes there may be several thousand butterflies clustered in one tree.

Navigation: Monarch butterflies, like some other insects, seem able to fly in certain directions as if they had built-in compasses. When a flock of Monarchs comes to a large city, a forest, or a mountain, they fly on over it, still going in the same direction. However, they often fly around large lakes rather than across them. For the purpose of our story, however, it is assumed that Monarch X and the rest of its flock flew southward across Lake Ontario. It is known that they often do this.

We do not know why Monarchs fly southward in autumn and northward in spring. Possibly it is an advantage for them to breed in cooler, northern climates where milkweed plants are abundant all summer. Of course, it is an advantage for the butterflies to fly south in autumn to avoid winter weather. How the butterflies "know" when to fly north or south is not fully understood. Recent research, however, indicates that the southbound flights of Monarchs begin when the hours of daylight become shorter in late summer. Some day perhaps we will also learn what it is that guides Monarchs on their flights. We think perhaps they are guided by the sun but we are not sure. Certainly, the Monarchs that fly south in autumn do not travel by familiar landmarks because they are not the same butterflies that came north in the spring. The spring flight was made by their grandparents or great grandparents.

INDEX

alligators, 29
autumn, migration in, 16, 62-63

bass, 34-35
birds, 25, 26, 46
breeding, 63
butterfly-weeds, nectar from, 25
buzzards, 52

California, roosting in, 63
Canada, 3, 11, 62
canyons, 24, 57
capture, 20-21, 57-60
Carolinas, 26
catbirds, 25
caterpillars, 62; and milk-weed leaves, 4, 6, 62; growth of, 4-5; description of, 5; to chrysalis, 6-7
Catorce, 57, 61
chrysalis, caterpillar to, 6-7, 62; description of, 8; to butterfly, 9
city, Monarchs over, 63
cloudless sulphur butterflies, migration of, 39
compasses, "built in," 22, 28, 63
cuckoos, 25
cypress trees, 29

Danaus plexippus, 62
daylight, shortening of, 16, 63
distance, traveled, 60-62; above ground, 20, 34

Eagle Pass, 49
east, migration toward, 39
eggs, laying of, 3, 62; hatching of, 4
egrets, 45
enemies, 20-21, 25, 26, 30, 35, 46, 60, 61; see also migration, difficulties of
Estacion Catorce, 57, 61

Florida, 63
flowers, nectar of, 16, 19, 20, 46, 56

forest, 29, 63
fuel, 27

Georgia, 28, 61
goldenrod, 27
Gulf Coast, 43, 63
Gulf of Mexico, 36, 61

Highland Creek, 11
horned owl, 33
hurricane, 43

Lake Ontario, 3, 16, 19, 63
Lake Pontchartrain, 42
lakes, 63
landmarks, 63
larva, 62
life history, 62
live oak, roosting in, 30, 34
Louisiana, 42, 45

map, of route, 40-41
mesquite bushes, roosting in, 46
Mexico, 49, 61, 62, 63; description of, 49, capture in, 57-60
migration, 16, 61, 62-63; difficulties of, 18, 42-43, 60, 61, see also enemies; direction of, 22, 24, 29, 39, 49, 63, see also east, south, north, west
milkweed, egg on, 3, 62; caterpillars and, 4, 6, 62
mountains, 22-23, 24, 51-52, 63

navigation, 63; see also migration
nectar, 16, 19, 20, 25, 27, 46, 56, 57
north, migration toward, 62-63
North American, flocks in, 62

Okefenokee Swamp, 28-29, 33, 36
Ontario, tagging in, 61, 63

Pacific Grove, roosting in, 63
palmettos, 38
Pascagoula Swamp, 38-39
pine grove, 23
prairies, 45
pupa, 62

railroad track, 56
rain, 18, 43
Rio Grande, 49
Rocky Mountains, 63
roosting, 12-13, 20, 30, 33, 36, 43, 46, 63
route, map of, 40-41
Royal Ontario Museum, 13, 15, 59-60

Sabinas River, 53
San Luis Potosi, 57, 61
scientific information, 62-63
shrews, 30, 32
Sierra Madre Mts., 51
south, migration toward, 16, 17, 19, 22, 24, 26, 28, 49, 52, 53, 61, 62-63
Spanish moss, 29
speed, of travel, 26
spring, migration in, 62-63
Station Fourteen, 57, 61
sun, as guide, 63
Suwannee River, 36

tagging, 13, 15, 58-60, 61, 62-63
Texas, 46, 49, 63
Toronto, 11, 13, 59-61
turtles, 29

United States, 61, 62
Urquhart, Dr. Fred, 61

Virginia, 25

west, 36, 39, 45
winds, 42-43
wings, 9, 11, 18, 30, 43, 60, 62
winter, avoidance of, 16, 63

zinnia, nectar from, 20